BRAIN BOOSTERS

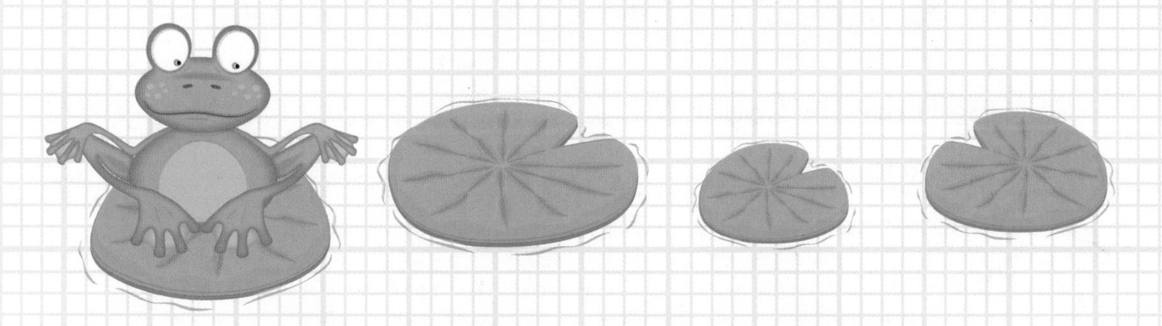

SUPER SMART

Number Puzzles

ARCTURUS

CONTENTS

TIPS ON NUMBER PUZZLES FROM SIR COUNTALOT

Read the instructions before you start. Some puzzles have more than one step.

Use your times tables to help you. They make things a lot easier!

Keep a pen and paper nearby to write down your answers. It is much easier to do this than to try to remember all the numbers along the way.

There are lots of different types of puzzles in this book! Challenge yourself with counting puzzles, multiplying and dividing questions, and logic tests. Which puzzles do you like best?

FLAMINGO FUN

How many flamingoes can you count?

And how many legs must there be?

If each flamingo eats 3 shrimps, how many shrimps is that?

Number-bot

This number-bot loves to play with numbers. Every number that enters his machine goes through three steps: First multiply by 2, then add 2, then divide by 2.

Number 6 enters the machine:
6 × 2 + 2 ÷ 2 = 7

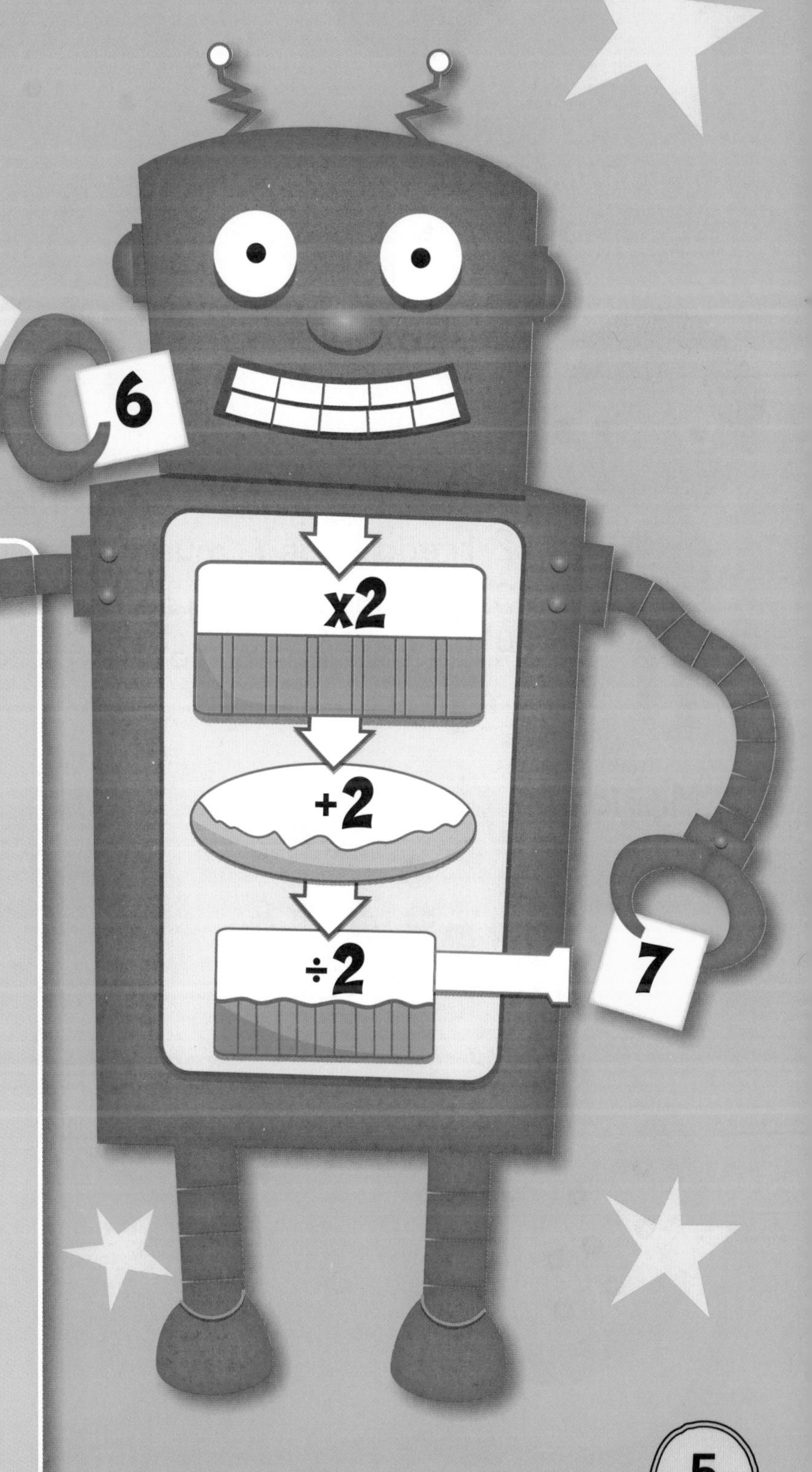

What will happen to the following numbers?

a 8

b 10

c 12

d 14

Look at what happens to the numbers after they have been through the machine. Can you see a pattern in the sequence of the answers?

PIZZA NIGHT!

These four friends are having pizza. Read the clues, then look at the pizzas to figure out which pizza belongs to which child.

1. Mario has eaten $^1/_2$ of his pizza.
2. Freddie has $^1/_2$ mushroom and $^1/_2$ cheese.
3. Roxanne has only eaten $^1/_8$ of her pizza so far.
4. Lola has eaten $^1/_4$ of her pizza.

Mario

Lola

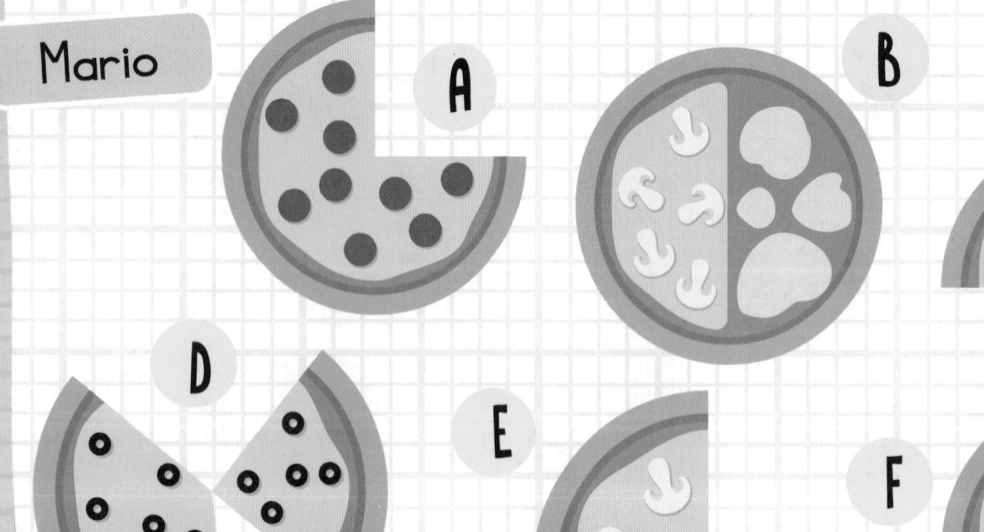

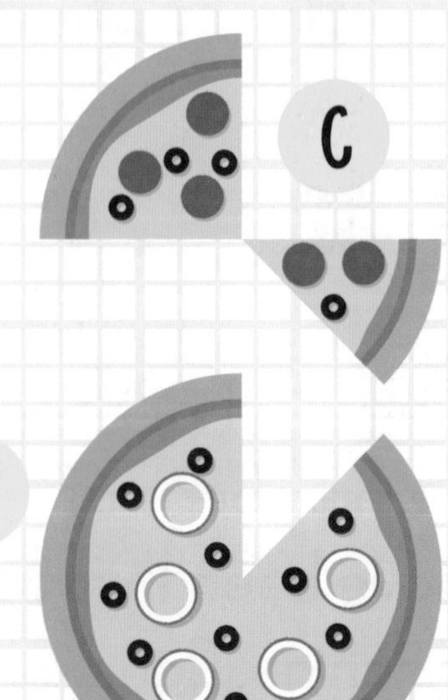

Guide the astronaut through space to the big purple planet, stopping at the planets that continue the number sequence.

PLANET HOPPING

BUILDING BRICKS

Beth the builder needs each vehicle to carry a load of 20 bricks to the building site. Match each vehicle with the correct load, so that they all have 20 bricks.

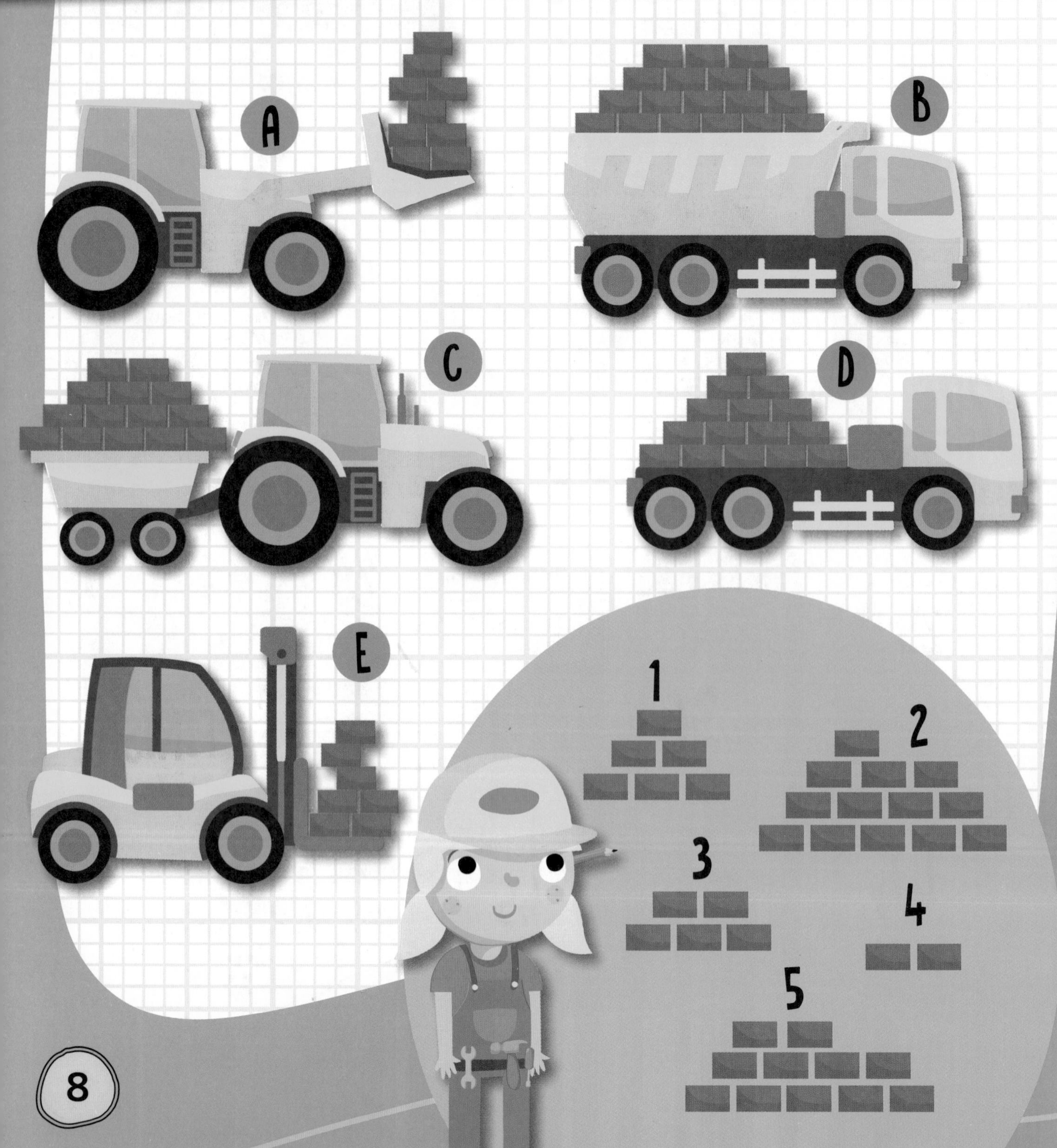

Racing Cars

Read the clues and solve the problems to figure out where each car finished in the race.

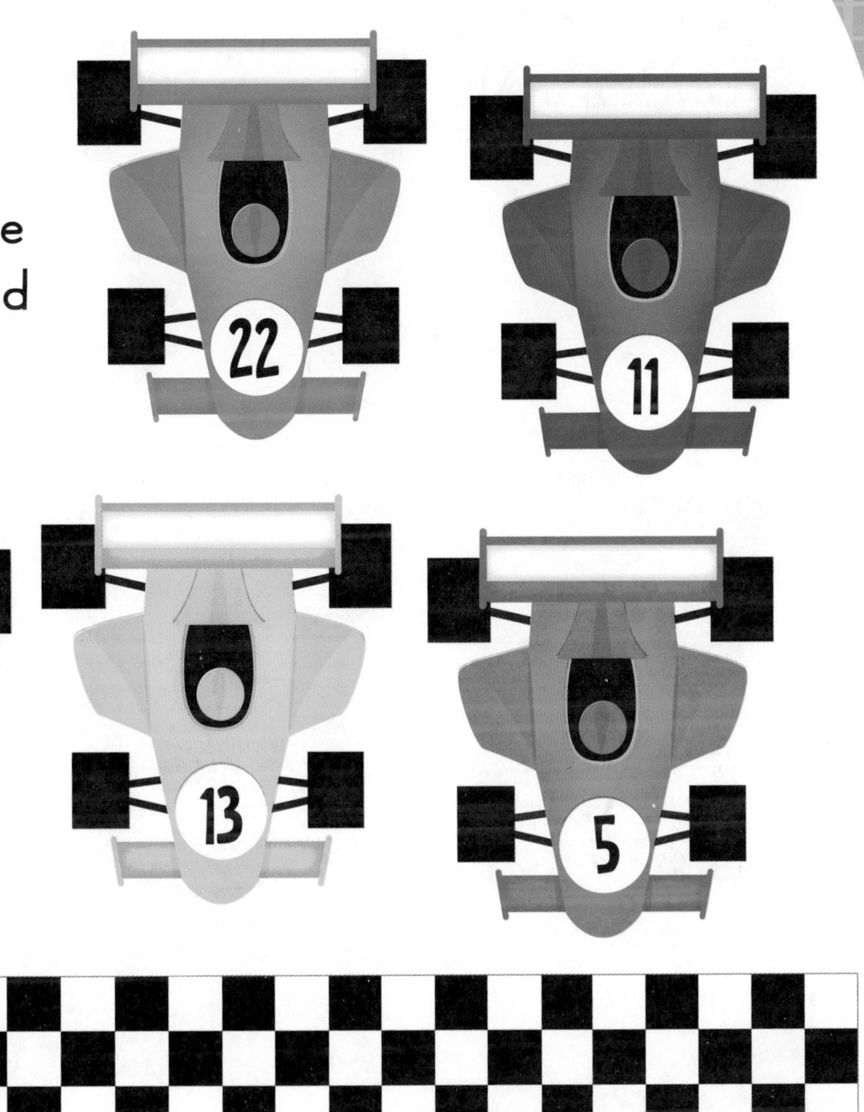

1. The winning car's number = 7x7.
2. Solve this problem to find second place: (8 + 3) x 2 = ?
3. The car in third place is the sixth prime number.
4. The car in fourth place is half of the second place car's number.
5. Solve this problem to find out which car finished last: 25 ÷ 5 = ?

HOUNDS THROUGH HISTORY

Sir Countalot's faithful hound, Henry, is always by his side. Sir Countalot's ancestors all had dogs, and here they are! Which hound lived the longest?

How many carrots will each bunny eat if they share them equally?

HUNGRY BUNNIES

FIRST PLACE

Mario, Freddie, Roxanne, and Lola have all taken part in a competition.

The friends have scored points for each event in which they took part. Look at the points board and the results.

	Points for 1st place	Points for 2nd place	Points for 3rd place	Points for 4th place
100m Sprint	100	75	50	25
Hurdles	80	60	40	20
Long jump	150	100	75	25

	100m Sprint	Hurdles	Long jump
Mario	3rd place	4th place	1st place
Freddie	4th place	2nd place	2nd place
Roxanne	1st place	1st place	4th place
Lola	2nd place	3rd place	3rd place

1 Which friend scored the highest number of points to win the overall winner's trophy?

Dino Plates

Look at the Stegosaurus plates. Which dinosaur has plates that add up to 5 x 5?

AGE ORDER

Friends Mario, Freddie, Roxanne, and Lola all have slightly different ages. Solve the sums to figure out the age of each friend.

LILY PAD LEAP

Guide Frank the Frog across the lily pads, leaping only on the lily pads which continue the number sequence.

FAIRY DOOR

Number 1:
The number of hours in a day divided by 4.

Number 2:
The number of months in a year divided by 4.

Number 3:
The number of tentacles on two octopuses, divided by 4.

Flora has forgotten the magical code to her fairy door! Solve the clues to figure out the four numbers in the code for her.

Number 4:
The number of legs on a spider divided by 4.

ROCK OF AGES

Use the clues to work out the age of each member of the Crag family. Hint: All their ages are even numbers.

CLUES

The mother is three times the age of her daughter and two years younger than her husband.

The father is more than 20 years older than his daughter.

The son is the youngest, and is one quarter of his dad's age.

FLYING HIGH

Figure out the number pattern on each flying thing, and work out what number replaces the question mark for each one.

AT THE BEACH

Match each child to his or her sandcastle by working out the answer to each problem.

BULLSEYE

Which of the archers has scored the most?

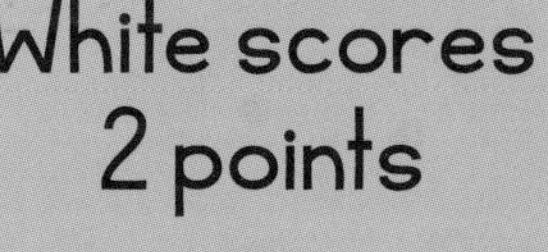

White scores 2 points

Black scores 4 points

Blue scores 6 points

Red scores 8 points

Gold scores 15 points

A

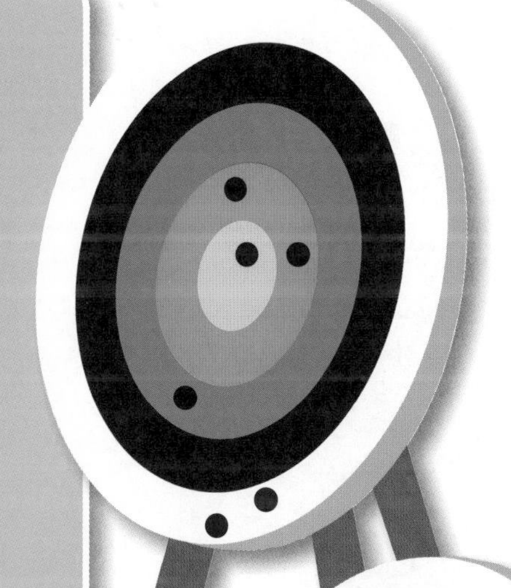

CROWN JEWELS

Share out the jewels so that each queen receives four red rubies, six green emeralds, and two blue sapphires.

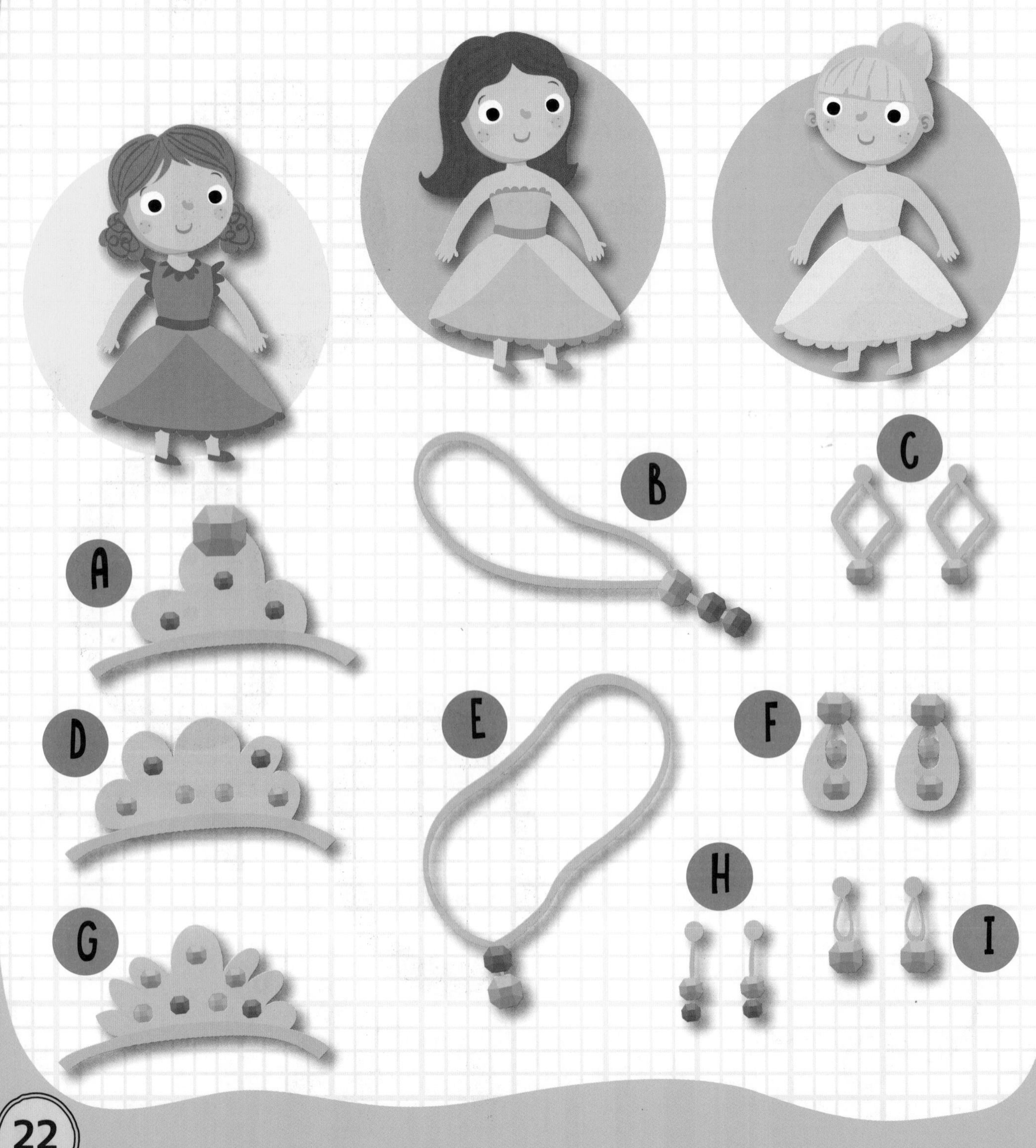

Deep Thoughts

Each sea creature represents the number 2, 5, 7, or 9. Work out which picture is which number to make the subtraction work.

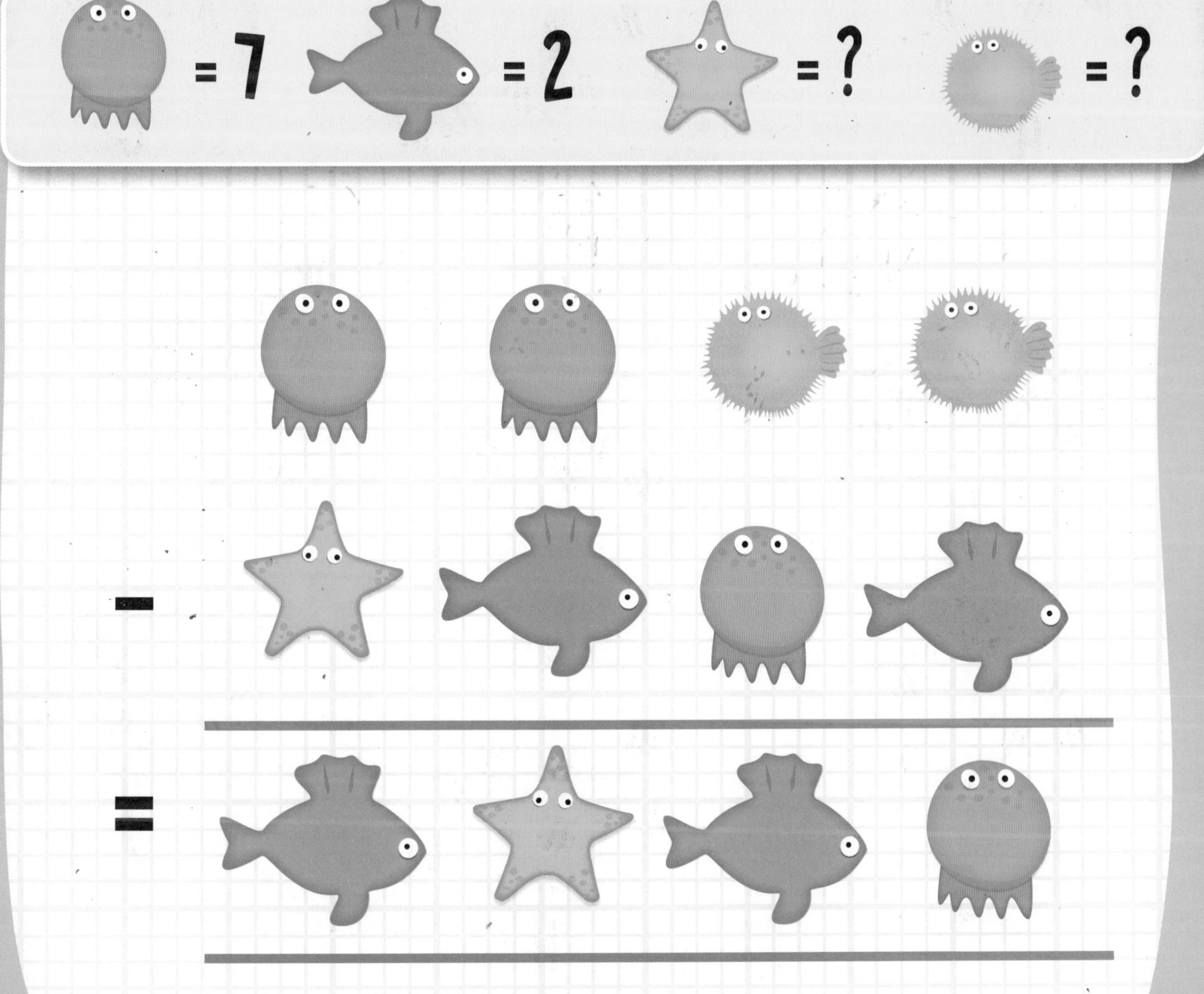

BUSY BEES

Pair up the honey pots that have the same number of bees around them. Which of the pots does not form part of a pair?

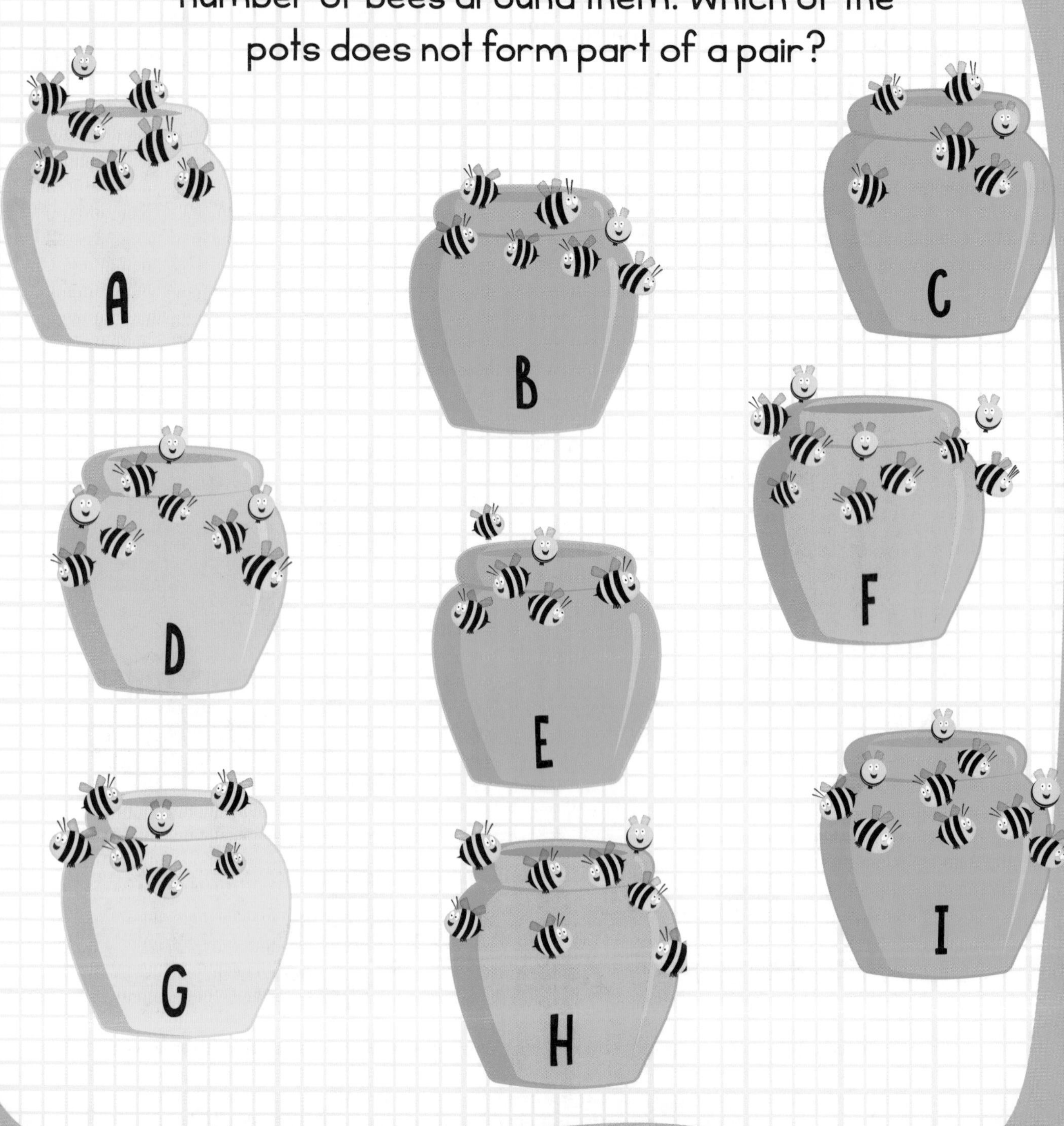

HEALTHY SNACKS

Count the fruit items and use your times tables to work out the answers to the questions.

1. How many apples in 4 baskets?
2. How many strawberries in 6 boxes?
3. How many bananas in 8 bunches?
4. How many oranges in 3 baskets?
5. How many grapes in 5 bunches?

OOH LA LA!

The friends are visiting Paris and buying souvenirs. Help them work out this problem.

Roxanne and Mario buy two models of the Eiffel Tower and one of the Arc de Triomphe. They spend 8 Euros.

Lola and Freddie buy three models of the Eiffel Tower and two of the Arc de Triomphe. It costs them 13 Euros.

If Freddie wants to buy an extra Eiffel Tower for his brother, how much money will he need?

WIN A PRIZE!

The school fundraiser has a prize for anyone who can guess the number of marbles in the jar. See if you can work out how many there are.

No one guesses exactly right, but the five nearest guesses are 50, 53, 62, 66, and 71. Of these guesses, one is 1 out, one is 3 out, one is 8 out, one is 10 out, and one is 13 out. How many marbles are in the jar?

IN THE BALANCE

See how the scales balance, and work out how many kangaroos would be needed to balance two zebras.

Answers

4. Flamingo Fun
15 flamingoes
30 legs
45 shrimps

5. Number-bot
a. 9 b. 11 c. 13 d. 15
The numbers increase
by one each time.

6. Pizza Night!
Mario: E
Freddie: B
Roxanne: F
Lola: A

7. Planet Hopping
1, 3, 6, 10, 15, 21, 28, 36, 45, 55
The sequence is:
+ 2 + 3 + 4 + 5 and so on.

8. Building Bricks
A = 5, B = 4, C = 1, D = 3, E = 2

9. Racing Cars
1st place: 49
2nd place: 22
3rd place: 13
4th place: 11
5th place: 5

10. Hounds Through History
Horace lived the longest.

11. Hungry Bunnies
They have four carrots
each (20 ÷ 5).

12. First Place
Mario scored 220 points, Freddie
scored 185 points, Roxanne scored
205 points, Lola scored 190 points.
Mario won the trophy.

14. Dino Plates
C

15. Age Order
Roxanne is 12, Freddie is 11, Mario is 10,
Lola is 13.

16. Lily Pad Leap
5, 10, 16, 21, 27, 32, 38, 43, 49, 54, 60,
65, 71, 76, 82
The sequence is:
+ 5 + 6 + 5 + 6

17. Fairy Door
6342

18. Rock of Ages
The mother is 30, the father is 32,
the daughter is 10, and the son is 8.

19. Flying High

A. 49 (double the gap between each number)

B. 78 (add multiples of 5 each time, so +5, +10, +15 and so on)

C. 9.875 (half the gap between each number)

20. At the Beach

$(3 \times 3) + 5 = 14$

$(8 \div 2) + 12 = 16$

$(4.5 \times 2) + 9 = 18$

$20 - (0.5 \times 10) = 15$

21. Bullseye

B

22. Crown Jewels

The jewels should be split into three groups:

A, E, F

B, C, G

D, H, I

23. Deep Thoughts

= 7

= 2

= 5

= 9

24. Busy Bees

D

25. Healthy Snacks

1. 28
2. 18
3. 24
4. 15
5. 55

26. Ooh La La!

3 Euros. Lola and Freddie buy an extra Tower and Arc, costing them 5 Euros more, meaning the price of a Tower and an Arc must add up to 5. The simplest way of solving this kind of puzzle is to guess at the prices for each item and work out how much the total would be. Then, make the prices larger or smaller depending on the answer.

27. Win a Prize!

63

28. In the Balance

One zebra = two tigers, and one tiger = two kangaroos. So two zebras = eight kangaroos.

Glossary

ancestor A relative who has lived a long time before you.

archer Someone who uses a bow and arrow in the sport of archery.

clue A small piece of information that may help you to find the answer to a problem.

equal The same on both sides.

Euro The currency of many European countries.

fundraiser An event held to raise money for a particular cause.

logic Using thought to think through a problem.

prime number A number that divides only into 1 and itself, for example, 2, 3, 5, 7, 11.

sequence A pattern of things, such as numbers, following each other in a particular order.

souvenir A small item that someone keeps to remind them of a particular place or time.

Further Information

Books

Colossal Creature Count by Daniel Limon, Barron's Educational Series, 2017.

Maths Quest: The Island of Tomorrow by Jonathon Litton, QED Publishing, 2017.

Over 80 Number Puzzles, Usborne Publishing, 2014.

Times Tables Puzzle and Activity Book, Arcturus Publishing, 2013.

Totally Brain-Busting Number Puzzles by Claire Sipi, Parragon, 2016.

Websites

www.bbc.co.uk/bitesize/ks2/maths/
Check out the BBC bitesize website for some fun maths activities.

www.mathplayground.com/games.html
Visit the Math Playground for more fun with numbers!

Index

This edition published in 2019 by Arcturus Publishing Limited
26/27 Bickels Yard, 151–153 Bermondsey Street,
London SE1 3HA

Edited by Kate Overy and Joe Harris
Written by Kate Overy
Illustrated by Ed Myer, and Graham Rich
Designed by Trudi Webb and Emma Randall
Cover designed by Ms Mousepenny

ISBN: 978-1-78950-300-5
CH006993NT
Supplier 33, Date 0119, Print run 8054

Printed in China